The Song of the Mantis

Written by Peter Garland
Photography by Peter Garland
Designed by Nicola Evans

03 02 01 00 99 98
11 10 9 8 7 6 5 4 3

Published by Shortland Publications Inc.
Produced by Shortland Publications,
2B Cawley Street, Ellerslie, Auckland, New Zealand
Distributed in Australia by Rigby Heinemann,
a division of Reed International Books Australia Pty Ltd.
ACN 001 002 357, 22 Salmon Street, Port Melbourne, Victoria 3207
Distributed in the United Kingdom by Kingscourt Publishing Limited,
P.O. Box 1427, Freepost, London W6 9BR

Printed through Bookbuilders Limited, Hong Kong.

ISBN: 0-7901-0924-7

THE
Song
OF THE
Mantis

**WRITTEN & PHOTOGRAPHED BY
PETER GARLAND**

I am born, breaking out
Of my winter-long wait
Into light.

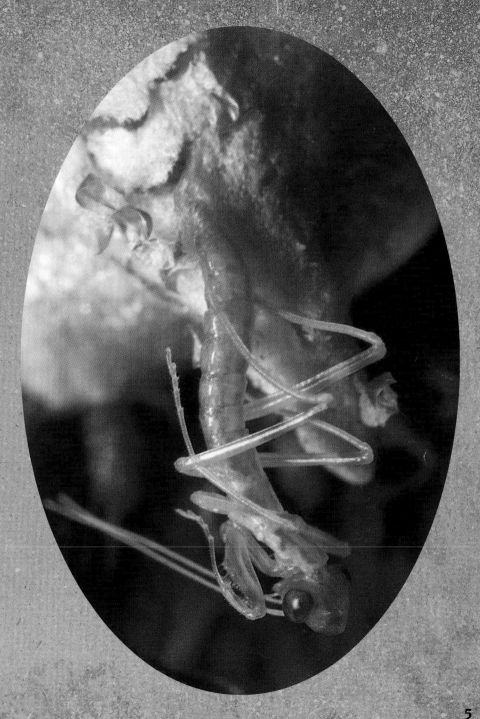

As still as the gentle
Falling of dew
Is my vigil.

In tune with the new
Season's tones, I choose
A green hue.

I abandon my skin
To the sun and the rain
And the wind.

M y new self feels splendid:
Loose-limbed and wonderfully
Slender.

I sleep in the open,
Steeped in dew, soaking
And frozen.

Could an eye, even near me,
Quite see me? An ear
Quite hear me?

I steal through haunts
Of leafy half-light
To hunt.

Green-gold are my eyes.
Stone-cold is their gaze
On my prey.

The law of the jungle
Is *war*. A *hunter*
Is *hunted*.

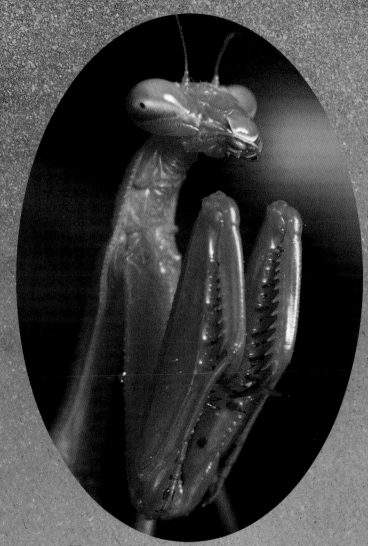

My forelegs are racks,
Drawn up to spring back
In attack.

The spider is doomed.
It will die, overwhelmed
By my storm.

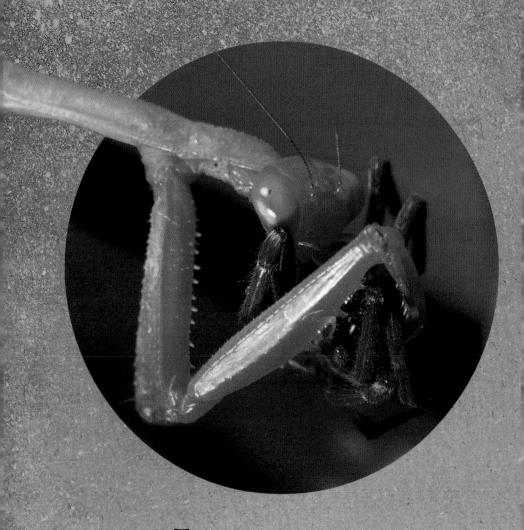

I savour the meat
That for days I have waited
To eat.

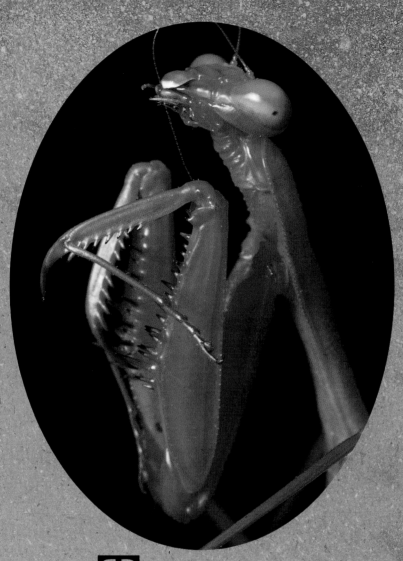

Then I tenderly clean
My antennae and tend
Every spine.

In the autumn I heed
Nature's call in all creatures
To breed.

I lumber, egg-laden,
Climb, find a snug place,
And lay.

23

In a wad of white foam

I swaddle my family

From harm.

T hen, hungry and too weak

To hunt, I seek

The sweet nectar.

For nature meets all
Of my needs in full,
Without fail...

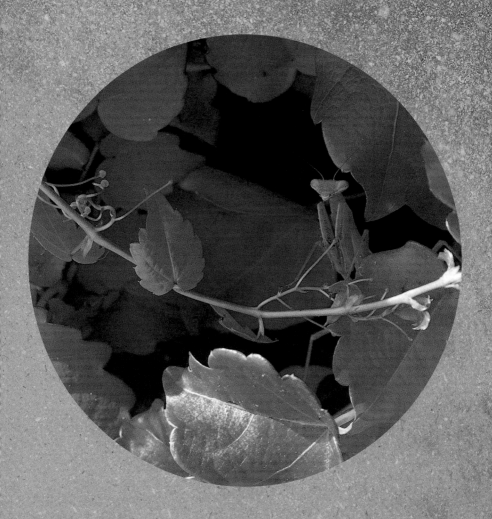

And at one with its splendour
And wonder, I blend
Into green.

FASCINATING FACTS ABOUT THE

Classification:
The mantis belongs to the net-winged order of the insect class. The mantis' scientific name is *Miomatis caffra*.

Appearance:
The South African mantis is distinguished by its long, slender *thorax* (part of the body between the neck and the abdomen).

Habitat:
The mantis is found worldwide in tropical and subtropical climates. It lives in long grass or low shrubs, where its colour, shape, and ability to "freeze" enable it to camouflage itself among the leaves.

Diet:
The mantis is a carnivore, preying on other insects and spiders.

SOUTH AFRICAN PRAYING MANTIS

Life Cycle:
Eggs are laid in a case, which the female mantis fastens
to a sheltered surface, like a tree-trunk, which is usually
some distance above the ground. Dozens of young
nymphs hatch the following spring. They resemble
much smaller versions of the adults. The nymphs grow
by moulting six times before becoming fully-developed
adults with wings.

Distinctive Features:
The mantis hunts by either stalking or waiting
motionless for its prey, which it suddenly snatches up
with its spine-edged forelegs. The front limbs are folded
while it waits to pounce, giving the mantis the
appearance of praying. This is why the insect has been
given the name *mantis*, which means "prophet".

BODY OF A PRAYING MANTIS

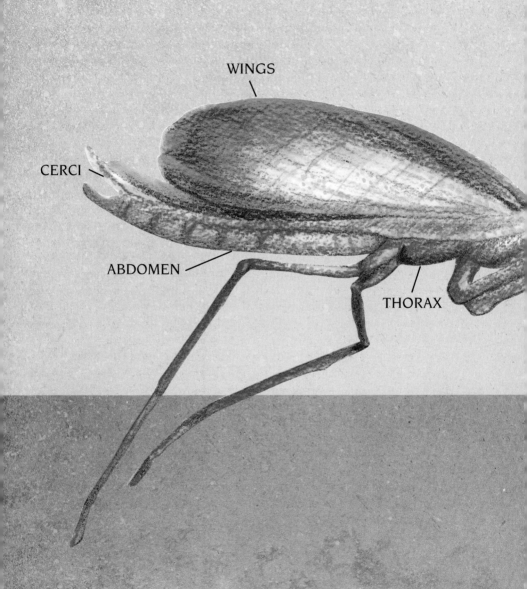

WINGS

CERCI

ABDOMEN

THORAX

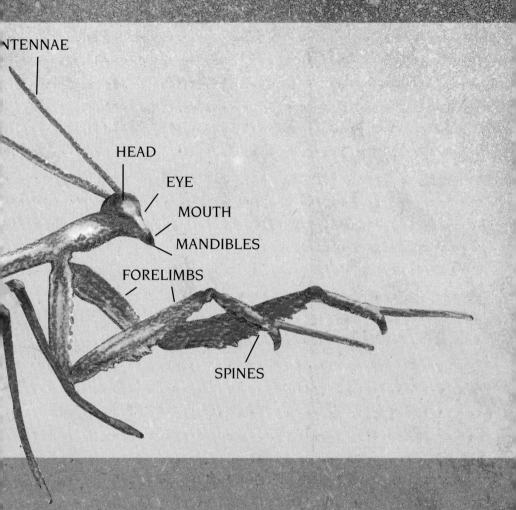

NTENNAE

HEAD

EYE

MOUTH

MANDIBLES

FORELIMBS

SPINES

TITLES IN THE SERIES